SCHOLASTIC

Essential English

Workbook 2

Material on pages 53 to 56 has earlier been published in *Reading & Maths K*, Scholastic Inc.; 2005

Published by Scholastic India Pvt. Ltd.
A subsidiary of Scholastic Inc., New York, 10012 (USA)
Publishers since 1920, with international operations in Canada, Australia,
New Zealand, the United Kingdom, India, and Hong Kong.

For information regarding permission, write to:
Scholastic India Pvt. Ltd.
A-27, Ground Floor, Bharti Sigma Centre
Infocity-1, Sector 34, Gurgaon (Haryana) - 122001
Email: info_in@scholastic.asia

Layout, design and typesetting FABLES

First edition: 2010
Reprint: 2010, 2011, 2012, 2013, 2014, 2015, 2016, 2018, 2024, 2026

ISBN-13: 978-81-8477-504-4

Contents

Introduction

Essential English is a set of innovative activity-based English books. The books use the communicative approach to help students improve their written and verbal skills and appreciate how the various elements of English are used to convey meaning. The course books, workbooks and teacher manuals follows the current NCERT curriculum and pedagogical principles and is designed to foster a love of literature and reading in children.

The student-friendly workbook contains additional exercises to complement and supplement the material in the course books. Each lesson in the course book has related worksheets. Each set of worksheets has three components—vocabulary, grammar and writing. The worksheets provide ample practice and aim to strengthen the concepts taught at each level. Additional crosswords are provided in workbooks 1 and 2.

These workbooks can be worked on at school or at home. The fun activities and attractive layout engage the student's attention and enhance the learning experience. The answers to the exercises are provided in the Teacher's Manual. We hope the *Essential English* workbooks will help students to communicate correctly and effectively.

1 Jay and the Baby

Vocabulary

Identify the pictures and fill in the blanks.

____

____

____

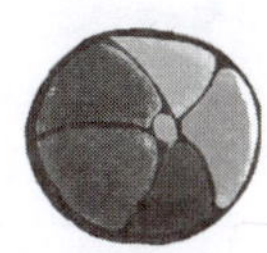

____

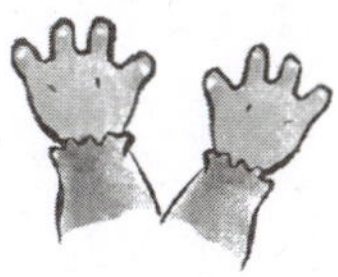

____

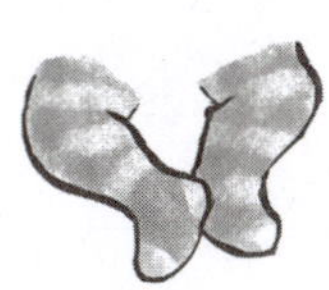

____

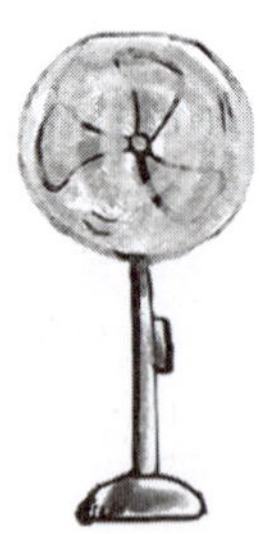

Grammar

Identify the pictures and write one describing word for each picture.

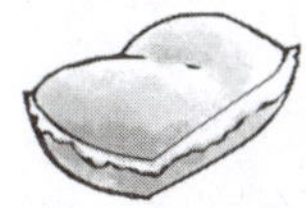

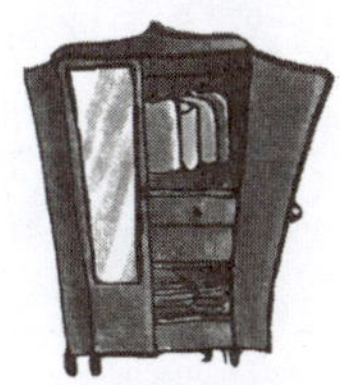

Writing

Read the story in the course book and find the names of some body parts.

________________ ________________

________________ ________________

________________ ________________

____

2 His Majesty's Moustache

Vocabulary

Write in the missing letters to complete the names of these months.

__anuary	__ebruary	__arch
__pril	__ay	__une
__uly	__ugust	__eptember
__ctober	__ovember	__ecember

Write singular nouns in each box to complete the chart. Three of the boxes have been filled in for you.

Nouns that end in ch, sh, ss, x	Nouns that end in y	Nouns that end in f
bench	party	loaf

Grammar

Complete each sentence with a common or proper noun.
In the box, write C if you wrote a common noun.
Write P if you wrote a proper noun.

1. I gave the book to __________. (person) ☐

2. Last summer I visited __________. (place) ☐

3. I love to eat __________. (thing) ☐

4. My aunt lives in __________. (place) ☐

5. I want a __________ on my birthday. (thing) ☐

6. My favourite festival is __________. (holiday) ☐

Read each sentence. Circle the singular noun and underline the plural noun.

1. The baby has small hands.
2. Rohan has two sisters.
3. I had an apple and a few almonds for breakfast.
4. My aunt picks tomatoes from her garden.
5. The farmer packs boxes with these different fruits.

Writing

Complete each sentence. Put in the correct punctuation mark at the end of each sentence.

1. Please let me ______________________________
2. Who is ______________________________
3. The garden ______________________________
4. Monkeys ______________________________
5. Where are ______________________________

3 Springtime on the Farm

Vocabulary

Follow the names of animals, people and objects that are found on a farm and find your way out of the maze.

cage	farmer	bus	pencil
kite	apple	hen	robot
book	car	duck	pond
carrot	ant	market	tractor
zoo	caterpillar	piglets	cow
jar	moth	cowshed	doctor
cockroach	bed bug	ducklings	sheep

Grammar

Read the postcard. Find the proper nouns and write them correctly on the blank lines below.

Postcard

kavita kapoor

11/2, green avenue

amritsar

india

Dear kavita,

It is very hot in chennai. we went to the marina beach and swam in the indian ocean. We visited the city of mahabalipuram. There we met rao uncle and his son, madhav. Tomorrow we are going to a hill station called ooty.

Love,

tanya

Write a sentence with a proper noun. Underline the capital letter or letters in the proper noun. Then write whether it names a person or a place.

Writing

Arrange the words to form complete sentences or questions. Keep in mind the punctuation.

1. seen you my shoes have

   ____

2. to the bank my took me dad

   ____

3. pond dog a jumped into a

   ____

4. a have can glass i water of

   ____

5. your name is what

   ____

4 A Dinosaur was at My Door

Vocabulary

Complete these sentences using words of your choice.

as strong as ________________

as thin as ________________

as white as ________________

as fit as ________________

as proud as ________________

as neat as ________________

Silent letters

- Silent g is followed by n.
- Silent u can be followed by e or i.
- Silent w is usually followed by r or h.
- Silent n comes after m.
- Silent b can follow m or be followed by t.
- Silent k is followed by n.
- Silent t usually comes after f or s.
- Silent h can follow c, g, k, r or w.

Use the rules above to add the missing silent letter to these words.

clim___	stomac____	wres___le
dou___t	cas___le	____nock
sc___ool	bisc___it	beni____n
autum____	fas___en	____ren

Grammar

Complete the sentences using **a** or **some** in the blanks.

1. There is ________luggage in the car.
2. There is _______ coin in my pocket.
3. There is ________ sand in her shoes.
4. There is ________ bathroom upstairs.
5. There is ________ oil in the bottle.

Circle the correct option.

1. Is eight **the/an/a** odd number or **a/an/the** even number?
2. I met Ravi at **a/an/the** Modern Store.
3. Would you like to have **a/an/the** apple or **a/an/the** banana?
4. Please get me **a/an/the** glass of water.
5. Mummy bought tickets for **a/an/the** latest film.

6. **A/An/The** school gates shut at 8 a.m.

7. Tomatoes are Rs 20 **a/an/the** kilo.

8. There is **a/an/the** new book on my desk.

Writing

Read the instructions and fill in the blanks.

1. Names of two vegetables that begin with c.

   __________ __________

2. Names of two vegetables that begin with p.

   __________ __________

3. Names of two vegetables that grow under the ground.

   __________ __________

4. Names of two green vegetables.

   __________ __________

5. Names of two vegetables that can be eaten raw.

______________ ______________

6. Names of two vegetables you like to eat.

______________ ______________

7. Names of two vegetables that you dislike.

______________ ______________

5 The Emperor and the Nightingale

Vocabulary

Underline the names of the objects you see in your kitchen. Circle the names of objects that you see in your bedroom and cross the names of the objects you see in the living room.

cushion	blanket	mug	telephone
shoes	plates	pillow	lamp
sink	fridge	spoons	carpet
painting	tap	cooker	pot
bed	kettle	bowls	sofa
teapot	table	butter	music player
television	jam	oven	chair

Grammar

Draw a line to match each masculine noun to its feminine noun.

nephew	mother
grandfather	aunt
man	princess
king	girl
boy	queen
uncle	niece
prince	grandmother
father	woman

Complete the table .

Masculine	Feminine
rooster	hen
	duck
peacock	
	doe
gander	
	cow
lion	
	ewe

Writing

Write two sentences about the emperor.

Write two sentences about the nightingale.

6 Eyes to See

Vocabulary

Complete these sentences with feeling words of your choice.

When I wear new clothes, I feel ____________.

When I lose something, I feel ____________.

When someone pushes me, I feel ____________.

When I get a star in my copy, I feel ____________.

Pick any two of your answers from above and draw a face that shows that feeling.

Grammar

Write the **–ly** form of the word given in the brackets to complete each sentence.

1. The snail is crawling ___________. (slow)
2. The man is driving __________. (careless)
3. It's raining __________ outside. (heavy)
4. The sun shines _________ in the afternoon. (bright)
5. Sonia writes _________ in her book. (neat)

Write a word with a similar meaning for each word. The first one has been done for you.

Word	New word with similar meaning
rapidly	quickly
silently	
merrily	
unhappily	

Writing

Write five sentences to describe a picnic. Draw five items in the box that you would take for a picnic

7 The Sun God

Vocabulary

Unscramble the letters and fill in the blanks.

1. I fight fires. I am a ________________. (ffreeigihrt)
2. I treat sick animals. I am a ________. (tve)
3. I look after the animals in a zoo. I am a ____________ (pzeokereo)
4. I cut and style people's hair. I am a _______________. (rbareb)
5. I teach students. I am a __________. (cetahre)

Grammar

Write the **–ing** form of these words.

1. comb ___________ 2. wash ___________
3. drink ___________ 4. cook ___________

5. cut ____________ 6. eat ______________

7. swim __________ 8. walk ____________

Circle the correct option.

1. Jyoti have/has large eyes.

2. Manu is happy. He has/have a new computer.

3. I has/have a lot of toys.

4. My uncle have/had an accident.

5. Rashid have/has/had high fever yesterday.

6. The postman have/has many letters.

7. My family and I has/have rice for dinner.

8. My pet rabbit only had/has a carrot a day.

Writing

Write the recipe for making a glass of lemonade.

Things I will need: ______________________

____

____

____

Steps:

____

____

____

____

____

8 In the Desert

Vocabulary

Find these weather-related words in the word jumble.

clouds	thunder	lightning
snow	wind	rain
sunny	rainbow	warm

A	R	F	Y	H	S	T	E	R	G
C	L	O	U	D	S	H	E	I	U
S	I	R	U	J	N	U	D	J	G
X	G	A	J	I	O	N	F	J	G
C	H	I	K	U	W	D	F	M	F
G	T	N	K	Y	C	E	G	R	D
Y	N	B	H	W	A	R	M	A	S
U	I	O	H	T	N	O	H	I	X
T	N	W	G	E	O	W	I	N	D
R	G	F	S	U	N	N	Y	L	N

Draw a picture of a rainy day.

Grammar

Use the **–d** or **-ed** forms of the words given in the brackets to fill in the blanks.

1. Last week an accident ______________ (happen) near our house.

2. It _____________ (rain) heavily last night.

3. I _____________ (reach) home late after the party.

4. Rohan _____________ (close) the door.

5. My mother _____________ (ask) me a question.

Read these sentences and complete the table.

1. My teacher ordered a large juice can.

2. The tall man walked in the rain.

3. Three kittens sat on the chair.

4. I held the pen in my left hand.

5. My elder brother goes to college.

6. We sat beneath a shady tree.

7. The black shorts have deep pockets.

8. The big book is on the doctor's table.

Naming words	Describing words

Writing

Your friend has come back after a vacation.
Frame five questions that you'll ask him/her.

____

____

____

____

____

9 The Owl and the Pussycat

Vocabulary

Circle the silent letters in these words.

bomb	rhyme	knife	wrong	write
knee	wriggle	know	lamb	sign
hymn	knob	honest	listen	comb

Grammar

Rewrite the sentences by inserting the missing doing words.

1. Humpty Dumpty on a wall.

   ____

2. Jack and Jill up the hill.

   ____

3. Mary a little lamb.

____

4. Little Jack Horner in a corner.

____

Underline the describing word or adjective in each sentence. Write the opposite of each adjective in the blank provided.

1. All my friends were happy. ____________
2. My house is next to the tall tree. ____________
3. The cups are on the top shelf. ____________
4. The witch lived in a large house. ____________
5. The boys ran fast. ____________
6. I had a glass of hot coffee. ____________

Writing

Read and finish this list. You can illustrate parts of the list in the boxes. Remember to listen to the sounds at the start of the words.

One wiggly worm,
Two terrible toads,

Three ____,

Four ____,

Five ____,

Six ____,

Seven ____,

Eight ____,

Nine ____,

Ten ____

watched the wicked witch.

10 Helen Keller

Vocabulary

The **-ing** forms of some doing words are given. Tick the word where the letter **e** was dropped to make the **-ing** form.

☐ brushing	☐ living	☐ laughing
☐ fishing	☐ swimming	☐ talking
☐ kicking	☐ climbing	☐ joking
☐ caring	☐ wading	☐ deciding

Grammar

What can these animals and people do? Think of as many doing words as you can. One is done for you.

horses
- eat
- kick
- gallop
- trot
- play

boys ______ ______ ______ ______

birds ______ ______ ______ ______

monkeys ______ ______ ______ ______

Underline the time words in these sentences.

1. My father sleeps in the afternoon.
2. I will watch a movie tomorrow.
3. Rajan and I went for a party yesterday.
4. My sister has a glass of milk every morning.
5. The teacher gave Mohan a gift last year.

Writing

Finish each sentence so that it answers the (question) indicated. The first one has been done for you.

The soccer players arrive in (**what**)

The soccer players arrive in a bus.

The cat takes a nap on (**where**)

____

The cookies were baked by (**whom**)

____

The dog was excited by (**why**)

____

The teacher came to the class (**when**)

____

I like to read (**what**)

____

11 Tiny Turtle Wants a Friend

Vocabulary

Fill in the names of these animals in the given boxes.

horse dog turtle mouse sheep

cow fish rabbit duck pig

cat snake frog chicken goat

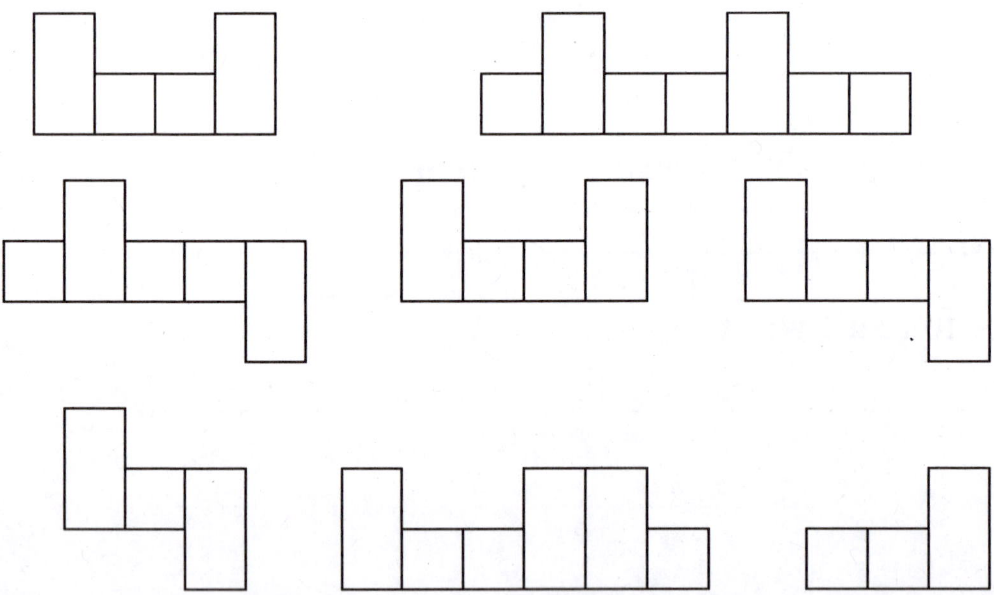

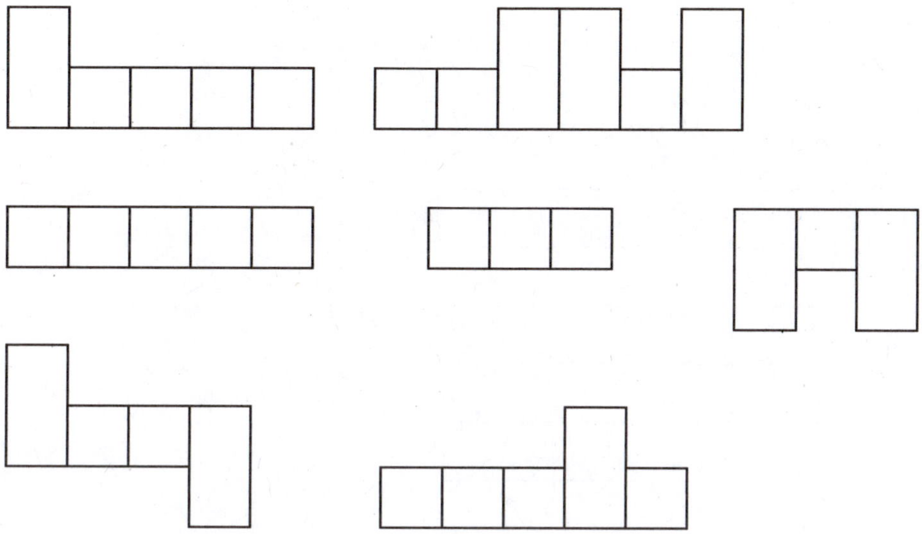

Grammar

Use the correct options to fill in the blanks.

1. Poonam ______ at home. (am/is/were/are)

2. I ______ reading the latest comic. (am/is/were/are)

3. My parents _________ watching a movie. (am/is/was/are)

4. Lalitha, my classmate, _____ a cute and chubby baby. (am/was/were/are)

5. Jyothi _______ my best friend. We ______ in the same class. (am/is/were/was)

Writing

You are going for a holiday with your friends.

I must pack: ______________________

____

____

____

____

____

____

____

____

____

____

____

12 Four Little Tigers

Vocabulary

Fill in the missing letter so that each word rhymes with **day**.

__ ay   h ___ y   sa ___

Fill in the missing letter so that each word rhymes with **mat**.

__ at   s ___ t   h a ___

Fill in the missing letter so that each word rhymes with **make**.

w__ ke   ___ ake   la ___ e

Fill in the missing letter so that each word rhymes with **bell**.

t__ ll   s e ___ l   ___ ell

Grammar

Decide which pronoun in the box can replace the underlined words. Write the pronoun on the line.

it we he she they

1. Mrs Singh is a popular teacher. ________________
2. Kiran and Monica shared some popcorn. __________
3. My brother enjoyed the movie. ___________
4. The glass fell and broke. __________
5. My mother and I learn Spanish. _____________

Fill in the blanks with any suitable pronoun.

1. Mihir has forgotten to bring _________ book to school.
2. I cannot find _________ clothes.
3. Arunima is playing with ________dog.

4. Mickey and Manu packed ________ bags.

5. Where are __________ books?

Writing

Draw an animal or bird and write a few sentences about it.

____

____

____

____

____

____

13 Sir No-name

Vocabulary

Complete the chart by naming the different modes of transportation.

air	land	water
____________	____________	____________
____________	____________	____________
____________	____________	____________
	____________	
	____________	

Grammar

Use these question words to fill in the blanks.

when where why what how

1. ____________ time is your class?

2. ____________ will you eat for dinner?

3. ____________ are your cousins arriving?

4. ____________ long do I have to wait?

5. ____________ are my glasses?

6. ___________ are you feeling now?

7. ___________ are you late for the class?

8. ___________ is in your bag?

Writing

Write a few sentences about your school bag.

____

____

____

____

____

____

____

14 How the Leopard Got its Spots

Vocabulary

Rewrite the sentences using words that mean the same as the words in *italics.*

The baby has *tiny* hands.

____

The question was *difficult*.

____

The movie will *begin* in five minutes.

____

Can you *shut* the window?

____

He doesn’t like to *chat* on the telephone.

____

Read each clue. Unscramble the letters and write the names of the animals.

1. This furry animal hibernates in the winter.
   ______________ RBEA

2. This bird uses its wings to swim.
   ______________ NGPEIUN

3. This sea creature has eight tentacles.
   ______________ CTOPSUO

4. This reptile has a long nose and sharp teeth.
   ___________ TARLILGOA

5. This wild animal has a mane.
   __________ LNOI

Grammar

Underline the prepositions in these sentences.

1. We ate the bread with cheese.
2. Rohan is standing on the chair.
3. She went to school at 8 a.m.

4. The rabbit ran into its hole.

5. I sat behind Vivek.

6. Ducks waddle in the lake.

7. We drove along the lake.

8. She has to do her homework in school.

Writing

Write a few facts about the largest land animal.

15 I'm a Real Boy

Vocabulary

Think of and write eight words that describe your school.

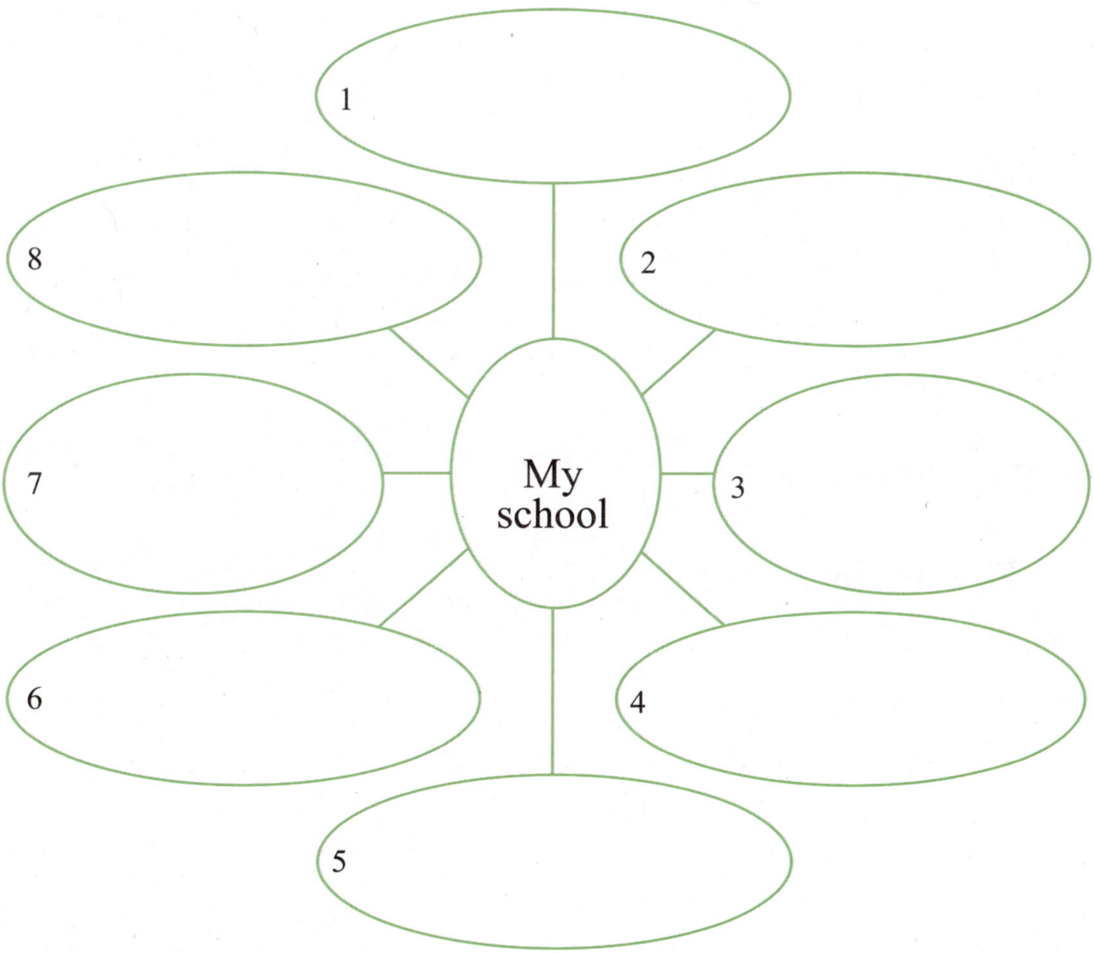

Grammar

Fill in the blanks with **or**, **but** or **and**.

1. Either Anita ____________________ Poonam will help mother.
2. The team tried hard ____________________ still lost the game.
3. Did Ranjit win ____________________ lose?
4. The judge spoke politely ____________________ firmly.
5. Uncle ____________________ aunty celebrated their wedding anniversary.
6. The story was long ____________________ interesting.
7. The baby either sleeps ____________________ eats.

Read these sentences and complete the table given on the next page.

1. Please come with me.
2. The boat sailed down the river.
3. The teacher wore a red dress and black shoes.
4. The kitten ran after the two mice.
5. Mother found my book under the bed.
6. Science is my favourite subject.
7. Cookies and chips were served at the party.
8. We saved the pennies in a box.
9. Their family visited Amritsar this winter.
10. Your new bag is in the room.

Nouns	Adjectives	Verbs	Pronouns	Prepositions

Writing

Complete these sentences.

I went to my friend's birthday party.

It was at ____

____.

We played ____

We ate ____.

We drank ____.

It was a __________________________ party.

Choose words from the Word Box to complete the crossword puzzle

Word Box

ant
bee
butterfly
ladybug
slug

Brady the brontosaurus has made a puzzle for you. Use the picture clues and the Word Box to help you

Word Box			
brain	bride	broom	bridge
bread	brush	bricks	bracelet

Across

2. 

4. 

6. 

8. 

Down

1. 

3. 

5. 

8.